KITE FLIGHT:
Theory and practice

KITE FLIGHT:
Theory and practice

Chris Wright

Middlesex University Press
London, England

First Published in 1999 by Middlesex University Press

Middlesex University Press is an imprint of
Middlesex University Services Limited,
Bounds Green Road, London N11 2NQ

A CIP catalogue record for this book is available from
The British Library

ISBN 1 898253 23 4

Manufacture coordinated in UK by Book in Hand Ltd,
London N6 5AH

Acknowledgements

This review could not have been written without help from a number of enthusiasts who know far more about kites than I do. I am particularly grateful to Paul Chapman for drawing attention to the role of discriminants in stability theory, and for passing on sources of information. Nicolas Wadsworth offered many stimulating ideas about stability generally, including the distinction between quasi-static equilibrium and dynamic stability and the application of dimensional analysis to the scaling problem. Together with Andrew Batchelor and Frank Wright, he drew attention to many errors in earlier drafts. Dan Leigh kindly provided a great deal of information and advice about different types of kite (especially deltas) together with various aspects of craftsmanship in kite construction. David Hughes and Frank Ogden provided valuable documentary material. Harm van Veen allowed me to see some of the illustrations in advance of the publication of his marvellous book (on essentially the same topic). I am also grateful to Joan Woollatt for collating other essential material, and to the librarians at the Royal Aeronautical Society and the Royal Society for their helpful cooperation.

CONTENTS

ILLUSTRATIONS

to Frank Wright

Figure 1: Different types of kite

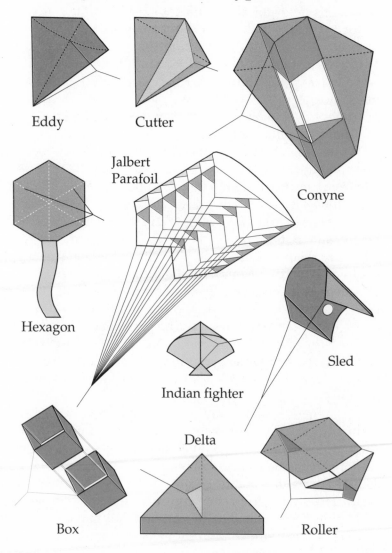

Eddy

Cutter

Conyne

Jalbert
Parafoil

Hexagon

Indian fighter

Sled

Delta

Box

Roller

INTRODUCTION

One of the attractions of kite-flying is that you can never be sure what will happen. If you buy a kite from a shop and the conditions are right, it will probably fly first time. If you're lucky it will stay in the air without any help, but it may need some adjustment, and it may not be obvious what to do. Furthermore things can get out of hand in a lively wind, and wear and tear will take its toll. After a few outings, even when built to a standard pattern, an old kite may need a fair amount of skill to keep it aloft. A home-made kite having an unusual shape may not fly at all.

While this adds to the fun it can also lead to disappointment: a pity because almost anyone can make a kite from plastic sheet, dowel, insulation tape and string, and enjoy flying it during any season of the year. There is a real challenge here: to evolve designs that stay put at a respectable height and if they don't, to build in simple methods for adjusting them until they do. Of course, there are plenty of books on how to design and build kites, but they assume that whatever you produce will fly perfectly first time. It rarely does, and they tell you little about what to do next, or even how to fly a kite at all. If you're an experienced kite builder puzzled by the behaviour of your latest creation, or a beginner about to launch your first kite and wondering how to make it work, this book is for you. It's a kite-flier's first aid manual.

Let's get under way by comparing the design requirements for a good kite with those for a good aircraft. Aircraft designers are concerned about performance: speed, carrying capacity, manoeuvrability and so on. They are also concerned about stability because if the pilot's attention is distracted away from the controls, the aircraft should preferably not spiral into the ground but carry on flying more-or-less in a straight line under its own accord. However, with modern stability augmentation systems this is no longer as important as it used to be.

Figure 2: Parts of a kite

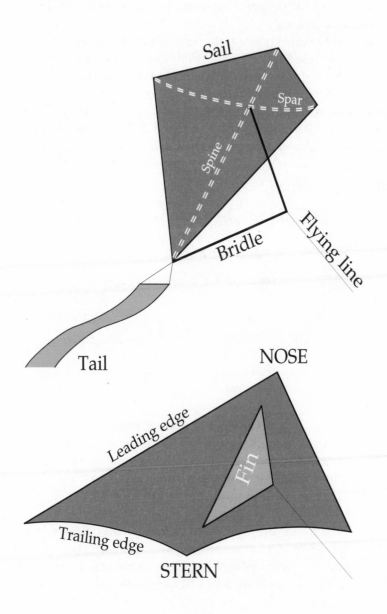

With single-line kites, it is the other way round. Since there's no pilot to apply those little corrections, stability is more important than anything else. Enthusiasts have differing opinions on why some kites are stable and others are not. Obviously, the shape is important: that's why kites are built to well-known patterns such as the Eddy, delta, box, and so on (see Figure 1 for different types of kite, and Figure 2 for the names given to their various parts). But for any given shape, it is not obvious what the proportions should be, nor how to modify them so that they work well. Popular books on kite-making usually stress the importance of *fins*, *tails*, *dihedral* and *adjustment of the towing point*, and these are so important we'll describe exactly what we mean by them now.

Figure 3: Different types of tail

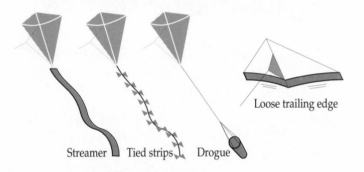

Streamer Tied strips Drogue Loose trailing edge

- FINS: for convenience we shall refer to keels, or any vertical panels sewn on underneath and used as attachment points for the flying line, as *fins* (see the cutter, parafoil, delta and roller types in Figure 1 and also the lower diagram in Figure 2).

- TAILS: are long strips of flexible material attached to the stern. Other stabilising devices can also be used, such as drogues, and if it flaps loosely in the wind, the trailing edge of the kite sail itself acts partly as a tail (see Figure 3).

- DIHEDRAL: has to do with the angle of the 'wings': although they may look flat on the ground, kites are not actually so in flight. Either the two halves of the sail are fixed at an angle to one another along their central axis to make a shallow V, or the sails bow upwards naturally under wind pressure (Figure 4), or they are bent upwards using a bowstring (there is one hidden behind the sail of the Eddy kite in Figure 2).

- ADJUSTMENT OF TOWING POINT: The point where the flying line is attached to the kite may be adjustable: many kites use a two-legged bridle with an attachment ring that can be moved along the bridle (Figure 5).

Figure 4: Dihedral

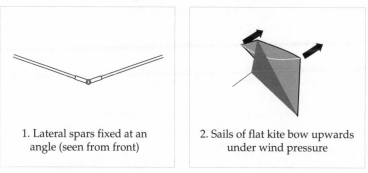

1. Lateral spars fixed at an angle (seen from front)

2. Sails of flat kite bow upwards under wind pressure

Figure 5: Adjustment of towing point

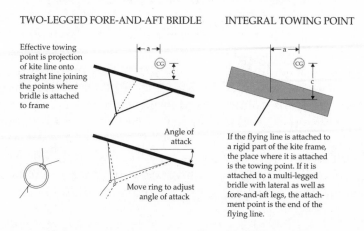

TWO-LEGGED FORE-AND-AFT BRIDLE

INTEGRAL TOWING POINT

Effective towing point is projection of kite line onto straight line joining the points where bridle is attached to frame

Angle of attack

Move ring to adjust angle of attack

If the flying line is attached to a rigid part of the kite frame, the place where it is attached is the towing point. If it is attached to a multi-legged bridle with lateral as well as fore-and-aft legs, the attachment point is the end of the flying line.

But *why* do these things affect stability, and *how*? When I started flying a few years ago, I was puzzled by the fact that some of my kites were steady and predictable in the air, while others were not. There seemed no rhyme or reason to their behaviour, and intuition didn't help. You would imagine that adding a fin to the rear of a kite would keep it pointing steadily into the wind, but it usually made things worse.

In fact, the problem was studied by aerodynamicists during the Second World War when the government was experimenting with kites and gliders for defence (Bryant, 1937; Bryant et al, 1942). One of the kites was built like a glider with wings, fuselage and tail, and in order to analyse it Bryant and his colleagues developed their stability theory from the existing theory for conventional aircraft. They concluded that the equations of motion for the kite and line were more complex than those for the free aeroplane. The results later came in useful, for example in the design of load-carrying parafoils during the 1960's (Nathe, 1967; Nicolaides et al, 1970). However, the theory is mathematically complicated and the explanations difficult to follow.

We shall not work through the mathematical theory, but instead try to show why it is important and set out the results in practical terms that kite-fliers can understand. We shall also draw together some other ideas on stability that aerodynamicists take for granted. There are two good reasons for doing so: the theory helps one understand what types of instability can occur and why, and some of the results are unexpected - they suggest remedies that one might not otherwise have thought of.

The book is divided into two parts. This first part deals with stability theory, and leads to some general conclusions about the features one should build into a design so that it will have a reasonable chance of success. It's not easy going but it's worth the effort (the glossary at the end may help). If you're not keen on theory, skip the first part and move straight on to Part 2. It is concerned with practical methods for adjusting a misbehaving kite so that it will fly better.

PART 1: THEORY

What do we mean by stability?

Let us start with a paradox. Why should a kite fly at all? Of course, it is driven by the aerodynamic 'lift' and 'drag' forces caused by air moving over and under the sail. (We often think of these forces as similar to those experienced by an aircraft wing, whereas in fact they are more complicated. The air doesn't just flow above and below the sails, but it also spills outwards like a ship's wake. The resulting pattern of movement is three-dimensional and not easy to picture – in fact, it wouldn't help much if we could, so that's all we're going to say about the aerodynamics of kite sails in this book.)

But it's not just a matter of aerodynamic forces. Imagine you have bought a new fence and you have left it propped against a tree while you look for some nails. What happens if the wind blows? Naturally, the fence keels over and falls to the ground. Most things fall to the ground if not firmly anchored, even things that are designed to float in the wind. Gliders sink. Frisbees flop. What is remarkable about kites is that they do *exactly the opposite*. Even more remarkable, it is their weight that keeps them the right way up – rather like a topsy-turvy pendulum. A weightless kite would not 'know' where the sky was, and would be just as happy flying on its side at ground level. As soon as we added weight, it would head straight up as far as it could go! I'm not aware of any other device that behaves in this way.

Of course, weight alone will not make a kite fly, and in practice we keep it to a minimum and concentrate on other things. Assuming that the wind is perfectly smooth and steady, and the kite is perfectly symmetrical about its centreline, then three distinct requirements must be met if it is to fly properly.

> (1) There must be an equilibrium position. This means that there must be a position in the sky where all the

forces and torques acting on the kite (including its own weight and the tension in the flying line) are in balance.

(2) It must be possible for the kite to climb to this position when launched from the ground.

(3) Having reached the equilibrium position, if the kite moves slightly out of line, the forces must carry it back to this position rather than making matters worse.

However, the wind is never perfectly smooth, and no kite is perfectly symmetrical because (a) there are always small defects in the construction, and (b) in any case the spars will bend and the sail material stretch unevenly under pressure from the wind. Consequently, we can add a fourth requirement that the design must be *forgiving* – it must work well even if the wind is 'bumpy' or turbulent, and its shape is slightly distorted. Some of these requirements can be met through adjustment. For the moment, we are concerned with something more fundamental. If a kite is not stable in the ways we are about to describe, no amount of adjustment will make it fly well – except perhaps by adding a tail that provides lots of drag as a last resort. Adjustment and tails will be left until Part 2.

Let us look again at requirements (1), (2) and (3). The first is easy to analyse; we can imagine the kite flying steadily at a fixed height and check what conditions are necessary for the forces acting on it to be in balance. The second is more complicated. For one thing, there might not be enough wind near the ground to produce lift-off (things usually improve higher up). Furthermore, kites tend to be less stable when attached to a short line. However, an experienced handler can usually persuade a difficult kite to climb a little way even if it comes straight back down again.

The third is the most complicated of all, and the most interesting. It is concerned with dynamic changes (ie, the way the kite moves in response to the forces), and we therefore refer to it as *dynamic stability*. Ideally, stability theory would

Fig 6: The six different ways a kite can move

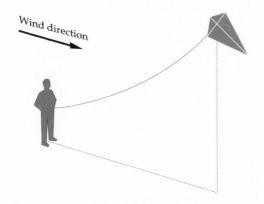

Wind direction

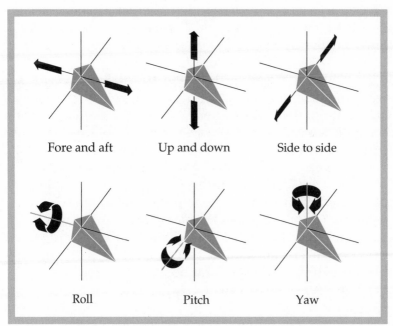

Fore and aft   Up and down   Side to side

Roll   Pitch   Yaw

enable us to predict in advance whether a new design were stable before it left the drawing board. The existing theory can't do this on its own – air movement around a kite sail is more complex than air movement around an aircraft wing. As well as flowing lengthwise across the upper and lower surfaces, it spills outwards on each side. Flexing of the sail is a further complication. Consequently, wind tunnel tests are needed to establish the aerodynamic characteristics needed to predict behaviour. Eventually, someone may solve the problem by writing a computer simulation package for kites, but a relatively powerful computer will be needed to run it.

What the theory can do, however, is highlight the design features that are helpful to stability in general terms. For example, it recommends a decent-sized vertical fin and has something to say about where it should be placed (not necessarily at the rear). It can't tell us exactly how big the fin should be, but if the finished kite doesn't work, it gives useful hints on what to do next (for example, make the fin bigger or smaller, or change its position).

A word of warning here: the theory (Bryant *et al* 1942) was originally developed for kites built like aeroplanes and hasn't progressed since then. Aeroplanes are rigid, with separate wings, a fin and a tailplane, all of which behave according to relatively straightforward aerodynamic rules. By comparison, toy kites are floppy and aerodynamically complicated. We assume, as a first approximation, that they behave in the same way as tethered gliders and are very cautious about the results. This may not seem very adventurous, but it's better than having no theory at all. Kites are peculiar creatures and I've not found guesswork very helpful in trying to make them do the things I want them to do – in fact it has often led me in the wrong direction altogether.

Now, a glider is a mechanical system with six 'degrees of freedom' – it can move independently along any of three axes, and also rotate about any of them (see Figure 6). A tail-less kite is just the same except that the volume of space in which it can move is limited by the length of its flying line.

The axes are initially fore-and-aft in the direction of the wind, up-down, and side-to-side. They are 'frozen' to the kite in its equilibrium position and move about with it thereafter. Movement in the side-to-side direction is termed sideslip, and it turns out to be especially important. All the rotations have particular names:

roll   rotation about the fore-and-aft axis
yaw   rotation about the up-down axis
pitch   rotation about the side-to-side axis.

Stability analysis can be simplified by grouping the movements together and considering each group of movements as a single problem. In effect there are two cases: lateral stability and longitudinal stability. Furthermore these two cases can be dealt with separately. Since lateral stability is the most difficult to achieve in practice, we will deal with it first. Only three types of movement are involved: sideslip, roll and yaw.

Lateral equilibrium

The first task is to check that there is an equilibrium position in the lateral sense, ie, from side-to-side. This is easy: a perfect kite is laterally symmetrical, so that if it is flying exactly downwind with the nose pointing straight at the handler, the lateral forces are balanced. However, this doesn't tell us how to get it into such a position, nor guarantee that even if we climbed a ladder and put it there, it would stay put.

Lateral stability

Given any particular starting position, the motion of the kite in sideslip, roll and yaw can be expressed in the form of three linear differential equations of the second order. They describe what happens when the kite moves a little bit in any of the three ways listed. Naturally, we hope the kite returns to equilibrium; it will then be stable, and we can examine the equations to see if this is the case. It is important to bear in mind though, that we are looking at small deviations here. Bumpy winds can produce large ones.

Figure 7: Two modes of instability in kites

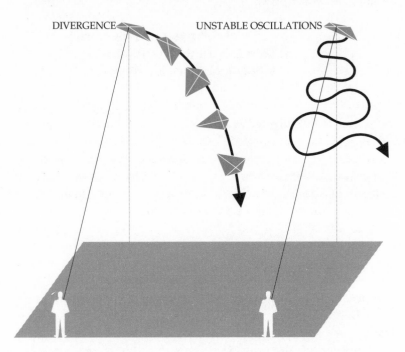

Unfortunately, a deviation from the initial position causes the aerodynamic forces to change in a complicated manner. The new forces may themselves produce new deviations of a different kind. For example, the changed forces resulting from a small amount of roll may themselves produce sideslip. The changes in force and the changes in position interact, so we can't look look at the three equations separately: they have to be solved simultaneously. In this particular case they can only have three types of solution (Frazer and Duncan, 1929), and according to the type of solution the kite will behave in one of three different ways. One of them is stable. The other two are unstable modes: an unstable 'divergence' and unstable oscillations.

The kite settles in a fixed equilibrium position STABLE

The kite 'sideslips', turns off-line and UNSTABLE
heads for the ground DIVERGENCE

The kite starts to wobble from side-to-side UNSTABLE
and the oscillations increase in amplitude OSCILLATIONS
until something awful happens

Figure 7 shows these diagramatically.

The equations are long-winded, and it's not necessary to solve them. Mathematicians won't: they are lazy and prefer simple formulae to lengthy calculations. To test for stability, it is enough to examine the coefficients of the equations and check whether they satisfy certain conditions. The coefficients are combined into simple mathematical expressions whose values can be positive, negative, or zero, and the sign determines whether or not the configuration is stable. These expressions are known as *discriminants.*

According to the theory, we can tell whether a kite is likely to suffer from unstable divergence or unstable oscillations by calculating the values of two of the discriminants. We will look at these in turn.

Unstable Divergence

Of course, any kite is liable to misbehave if it is distorted in shape, roughly handled, or disturbed by a turbulent wind. But in theory, a 'divergent' kite always turns over even when it is perfectly symmetrical and the wind is perfectly steady, rather like a ball-bearing poised on top of a football. No matter how carefully we place the ballbearing at top dead-centre, the slightest disturbance such as an ant stamping on the ground in Brazil will shake it off. What happens next is outside the scope of the theory: some kites power-dive into the ground while others such as the Indian fighter keep turning and start to spin. With practice, one may be able to avoid a crash by quickly paying out the line, or running forward. But after the kite regains altitude the cycle will start again, and repeat itself until one runs out of line or out of room.

In its simplest form, the condition for non-divergence with glider types of kite can be written:

$$cn_V + al_V < 0 \qquad \qquad \ldots (1)$$

where a and c are the distances of the effective towing point respectively forward of and below the centre of gravity (CG) of the kite when flying in its equilibrium position (see Figure 5). The effective towing point is the point at which, for stability purposes, the flying line is considered to be attached to the kite frame, and since this must be forward of and below the CG, a and c are both positive. We shall have more to say about this, together with the location of the effective towing point, later.

The terms n_V and l_V are dimensionless coefficients that represent forces on the kite arising from sideslip. More accurately, the term l_V is proportional to the rate of increase in the torque about the fore-and-aft axis through the CG (the twisting force that makes a kite roll) with *sideslip* v (the component of wind velocity sideways on to the kite). This is a bit of a mouthful; think of l_V as the propensity of a kite to roll over when the wind blows at it from one side. The larger its value, the more readily will the kite roll over, like a tramcar caught in a sideways gust. Although it is not standard nomenclature, we shall call l_V 'roll-over' for short. If we had a wind tunnel, we could estimate its value by plotting the torque on a graph for different angles of sideslip, and measuring the slope of the curve.

The term n_V is the rate of increase in the yawing torque about the vertical axis through the CG with v. Again, this a mouthful, so think of it as the propensity to 'weathercock', or turn into the wind when its direction changes. For some aerodynamic devices such as darts and arrows it has to be positive, otherwise they will turn away from the direction they are travelling in and miss the target. This is why darts and arrows (and weathercocks) have fins at the rear.

Surprisingly, however, positive weathercocking encourages divergent instability in kites, because we need the sum of the two terms on the left-hand side of equation (1) to be *negative*. The reason is that when it slips to one side, the wind forces on the kite will tend to make it turn or yaw into the direction of sideslip, and keep going. Whereas other deviations produce forces that tend to restore the kite to its original position, sideslip may, if there is too much weathercocking, simply get worse. It is therefore critical for stability.

As it happens, for most kites the roll-over term l_v comes to the rescue. Their dihedral makes them roll away from the direction of sideslip because the wind gets under the leading wing and lifts it up, making l_v negative. We have tried to show this effect schematically in Figure 8, although in real life the events shown occur simultaneously and not as a sequence of four separate stages.

Figure 8: How dihedral combats sideslip

(Schematic representation only)

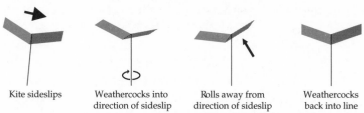

| Kite sideslips | Weathercocks into direction of sideslip | Rolls away from direction of sideslip | Weathercocks back into line |

Consequently, for kites with dihedral a certain amount of positive weather-cocking can be accommodated provided the roll-over term is sufficiently large to make the sum of the two terms in equation (1) negative. The situation for box kites is different: with little or no dihedral l_v is probably close to zero.

However, they do seem to have negative weathercocking, so equation (1) is still satisfied. Why then, you may ask, don't they turn round and fly backwards? The answer seems to be that the term n_v is concerned with yaw about the *centre of gravity* – the theory was originally developed for aircraft in free flight. Unlike aircraft, kites are constrained by the flying line to pivot around the *effective towing point*, which is further forward than the CG. Hence a small negative n_v can be tolerated provided that the sideways wind force that causes them to yaw lies astern of the towing point.

We can now return to the dimensions **a** and **c**. These define how the line is attached to the kite relative to the CG. If the towing point forms part of the rigid structure of the kite, or, what amounts to the same thing, the bridle is restrained from moving laterally relative to the kite body (see Figure 16 for two examples of kites with lateral bridles), the measurements are made from the towing point itself. However if the kite has a conventional two-legged bridle, which is not restrained in the side-to-side direction, the effective towing point as far as lateral stability is concerned is the projection of the flying line onto the kite body as shown in the left-hand diagram in Figure 5 (strictly speaking it is the projection onto a straight line joining the bridle attachment points).

From equation (1), we see that **a** and **c** act as multipliers. If we change the shape of the bridle we can increase or decrease their value in such a way as to magnify the effects of any negative terms in equation (1) and diminish the effect of any positive ones, so that the sum of the two terms takes on the largest possible negative value. (Box kites are different from most other types because they have negative weathercocking, and the rollover coefficient is close to zero so it has little effect. All we need to do is make **c** large. In other words, we lengthen the bridle legs.)

Now the majority of kites have dihedral, which produces negative roll-over whose effect can be magnified by making **a** large. They also have positive weathercocking, which is *not* desirable, so we reduce its effect by making **c** small. Together, these amount to moving the towing point forward and upward. If the kite has a two-legged fore-and-aft bridle, this can conveniently be done by shortening the whole bridle and moving the attachment point towards the nose.

However, this can lead to other problems: as experienced fliers will be aware, a forward towing point will reduce the height at which the kite will fly on a given length of line, and as we shall see in a moment, it is liable to produce unstable oscillations.

UNSTABLE OSCILLATIONS

Unstable oscillations are just as exciting to watch as divergence. If they are not controlled by letting the line go slack, the kite will swoop further and further from side to side until it turns right over, and possibly continues to spin round in small circles, losing altitude until it crashes. The condition for oscillations not to occur with glider types of kite can be expressed approximately as

$$\mu(cn_V + al_V) + y_V(cn_r + al_r) > 0 \qquad \ldots (2)$$

where the dimensionless term μ represents the wing loading (it is actually twice the mass of the kite divided by three other quantities – the total sail area, the density of air, and the kite wingspan or width between the sail tips). The term y_V is also a dimensionless coefficient whose value is proportional to the rate of change of lateral force on the kite with lateral velocity: it expresses the pushing effect of a sideways wind component. It is always positive.

The terms n_r and l_r are analogous to n_V and l_V: they are proportional to the rates of change of the yawing and rolling torque respectively, this time with respect to angular velocity in yaw. They express the changes in the aerodynamic forces on the kite that arise if for some reason it happens to spin (or yaw) about its vertical axis through the CG.

We have already met the expression inside the first set of brackets in equation (2): it is the same as the expression on the left-hand side of equation (1), which must be negative if the divergence condition is to be satisfied. To prevent unstable oscillations, therefore, we need the first term to be numerically small and the second term to be positive and numerically larger than the first. Since the first set of brackets is multiplied by μ, we must keep μ small: this means keeping the weight down, or increasing the sail area.

The second bracket in equation (2) is multiplied by y_v, and therefore large y_v is helpful. This implies lots of vertical surface so that the kite resists being pushed sideways. Dihedral has this effect and it is helpful in combatting divergence too. Alternatively, one can use a large fin area or a combination of the two.

Unfortunately, l_r is usually negative (at least for glider types of kite), so everything now depends on n_r. Crudely, we can think of n_r as the resistance of the kite to spinning in yaw, and the conclusion is straightforward: we need a large area of fin placed like paddlewheel blades as far away as possible from the CG to increase the kite's resistance to being pushed round against the air. Since the non-divergence condition places an upper limit on the amount of 'weathercocking', it may not be helpful to have all the fin area at the stern: if more is needed, it should be shared between the front and the rear. In practice, very few kites are built with two fins because of the extra weight: the parafoil together with some types of roller are notable exceptions (see Figure 1).

Again, dihedral provides an alternative – it supplies the equivalent of vertical surface area and therefore can act to some extent like a fin. However, the requirement to concentrate this vertical surface at the nose and stern appears to rule out kites with long, narrow wings like aeroplanes or hang-gliders. For reasons that we can't go into now, such high *aspect ratio* wings are aerodynamically efficient in the sense that they produce much lift and little drag, but they are not suitable for a kite unless we are prepared to extend the spine and add fins at the front and rear, or have two separate wings, one at the nose and the other at the stern.

This may explain why the wingspan of a successful kite is rarely greater than its length from nose to stern: the two are usually about equal, even for rollers and parafoils. Of all the standard forms, only deltas seem to manage with a large wingspan (around twice their length) without oscillating, possibly because the oscillations are damped through the large concentration of sail area at the stern (see below): in any case the outer part of the sail adopts a reduced angle of attack – 'washout' – which alters the aerodynamic characteristics of the kite in ways that are outside our scope here.

A second alternative is to add a tail, which also tends to damp out yaw. A third is to design the kite with areas of loosely tensioned sail near the stern that absorb energy by flapping in wind. Their extra drag has a similar effect to a tail or drogue, adding further to the stability of delta kites in particular. It is widely believed that using an old-fashioned porous material such as cotton for the kite sail instead of modern rip-stop nylon also contributes to stability, perhaps because of the increased drag.

The only other possibility is to move the towing point. Since we need to reduce the influence of the negative term l_r, **a** should be small compared with **c**. In other words, the distance of the attachment point forward of the CG should be as small as possible (the opposite of what is needed for stability against divergence).

OTHER FORMS OF LATERAL OSCILLATION

Cutter kites have a large fin and oscillate laterally in a different way, possibly because wind eddies form alternately on opposite sides. The oscillations are limited in size and the kite doesn't crash, but a lot of energy is wasted and the kite doesn't fly as high as it would otherwise do. Also, Eddys and other diamond-shaped kites are liable to sway from side to side when the wind drops and the amount of lift becomes barely sufficient to keep them in the air. But if a kite is likely to come down anyway, it is probably better to do so in the manner of a falling leaf than a dead duck.

SCALING

I once made a kite from a dustbin bag and then set about developing it into a kit for school pupils to make from printed sheets that were appreciably smaller than the original one. Unfortunately, although the original worked well, the 'production' version caused a lot of trouble. Can one predict the stability of a kite that is scaled up or down to a different size?

In fact, there are several problems here. Suppose we are making a bigger version. The first problem is structural – we have to choose the thickness of the new spars so that (a) they don't break, and (b) they flex or deflect the right amount. Now, at a given wind speed the aerodynamic forces on the kite are proportional to the area of the sail, so if the new wingspan is f times the old one, the forces will increase by a factor f^2.

Structural engineers know that the stresses in a structure are proportional to the forces divided by the cross-sectional areas of its members. It follows that if we choose the new spar thicknesses so that they scale up in the same ratio f as the size of the sail, then their cross-sectional area will be scaled by a factor of f^2 and hence the new maximum stress will increase by a factor f^2 divided by f^2 – in other words it will remain unchanged. Assuming that we are using the same spar material, this is just what we want.

The same would apply to the sail fabric if we could get it in different thicknesses: scaling the thickness up or down in proportion to the size of the sail would ensure that the stresses were unchanged. In practice, kite makers tend to use a standard gauge of ripstop nylon for a range of designs because it is readily available. Consequently, if a kite is scaled up in size the stresses will increase and there is a risk that the fabric will tear. But we can get round this by reinforcing the sail where the stresses are highest.

So far so good. What about deflection? It turns out that deflections in the spars are proportional to (force x length^3)/(second moment of area) where 'second moment of area' is a property of the spar cross-section that is proportional to f^4. The deflections will therefore increase by a factor $(f^2 \times f^3)/f^4 = f$. In other words, they will scale up in the same proportion as the size of the kite. This seems reasonable:

the new kite will have the same degree of 'stiffness' as the old one inasmuch as the spars will curve exactly the same amount *in relation to their length*.

Now we can tackle the stability problem. Nicolas Wadsworth (1995) has used a technique called dimensional analysis to throw light on this. The same result can be deduced from the Bryant *et al* (1942) analysis. All the variables in equation (1) except **a** and **c** are dimensionless, that is to say, they have no physical units, but more importantly, their values are unaffected if the kite is scaled up or down in size. Furthermore, if we scale **a** and **c** in the same ratio, their relative values are unaffected and the sign of the expression on the left hand size can't change. Therefore, if a kite is stable in divergence, in theory it can safely be scaled up or down in size.

We cannot say the same about unstable oscillations. Whereas all the other terms in equation (2) retain their original values after scaling, the dimensionless term μ may not. It is proportional to the mass of the kite divided by f^3. Everything therefore depends on whether μ increases or decreases, which depends in turn on whether the mass increases in proportion to f^3. Spars are no problem if we change their thickness as suggested earlier, because their mass will then be exactly proportion to f^3. It's the sail material that's the problem because there are not many standard thicknesses of ripstop material. If we use one standard thickness throughout, the mass of the sail will then be proportional to its *area*, so that in scaling up, the value of μ *decreases*. This is fine, because we want it to be as small as possible – the kite will actually be more stable. But if we scale down, μ *increases*, and we risk running into stability problems. Nicolas Wadsworth (1995) has demonstrated this by making miniature box kites in several different sizes out of the same thickness of paper. While the larger ones were stable, the smaller ones oscillated.

Of course, stability is not the only consideration when scaling up or down. In particular, if we make a kite bigger according to the above criteria its weight will increase more than its area (by f^3 as opposed to f^2). So in general, larger kites need a greater minimum wind speed to keep them aloft, whereas in stipulating a constant wind speed, we have assumed a value sufficiently large to lift the scaled-up kite as well as the original. Were this not the case, we would have to lighten the kite, risking increased stresses and the possibility of breakage. Contrary perhaps to what one might expect, large kites can pose structural problems, and in this sense they are less efficient than small ones.

Summary: design requirements for a laterally stable kite

Let us try to piece all this together. We have to satisfy two lateral stability conditions using three main tools: fins, dihedral, and adjustment of the towing point (we shall leave tails until Part 2). Since we don't have a wind tunnel, and the coefficients in the stability equations are difficult to estimate in any other way, we can't specify in advance how much dihedral to build into the design, nor how large the fin(s) should be. But the theory tells us in principle what to look for, and how to improve an unsuccessful design.

(a) DIHEDRAL provides the rolling torque in sideslip that is necessary to avoid divergence. It also allows the sail itself to act partly as a vertical surface and hence damp out unstable oscillations. If the area of the sail is concentrated only towards the stern of the kite like a delta, it also contributes to weathercocking but may then lead to divergence. For other kites, the requirement to damp out yawing oscillations appears to rule out a wing span that is greater than the fore-and-aft length.

(b) FINS provide resistance both to sideslip and to yaw, both of which help to prevent unstable oscillations. Where possible, the fin area should be split between the nose and stern so as to maximise resistance to yaw, with enough at the stern to provide positive weathercocking but not so much as to compromise divergent stability.

(c) The TOWING POINT is subject to conflicting requirements. For a 'dihedral' kite that diverges but does not oscillate, it could be moved forward. For a kite that oscillates but does not diverge, it could be moved back, as close as possible to the CG. In practice, aerodynamicists recommend the latter: moving it forward seems to have only a limited effect, and in any case most kites fly at a higher angle of elevation with the towing point set close to the CG (see Part 2: this also helps to prevent overshoot).

Finally, the theory tells us that a heavy kite is an oscillating kite: make it bigger but in the same fabric or a lighter one, and keep the weight of the spars down.

Does lateral stability theory work?

Ordinary toy kites differ from rigid gliders in so many ways that we ought to ask whether the theory is relevant – does it explain their behaviour? Well, we can list the various types of kite that are commonly in use together with the forms of instability to which they are prone, and see if they tally with the theoretical predictions. Among the conventional types, only a few seem prone to unstable oscillations. All the rest are prone to divergence, or neither. The types we shall consider are shown in Figure 1 (unfortunately, the theory does not apply to sled kites, because they are nothing like aeroplanes).

EDDY: this kite has dihedral but no fin. The dihedral provides rolling torque in sideslip and not much weathercocking so one would predict that an Eddy is not liable to divergence. However, since the effective vertical surface is not concentrated at the nose or stern there is little resistance to yawing and one might expect it to be prone to unstable oscillations, which is indeed the case. Interestingly, this only occurs when the towing point is too far forward, which is again what the theory predicts.

DELTA: divergence can be a problem among older delta kites, possibly because of the concentration of sail area towards the stern – when deformed by the wind, this acts partly as a vertical surface which, the theory predicts, could induce increased weathercocking and hence divergence. Deltas are much happier when flown with a tail.

CONYNE: Conyne kites are stable under a wide range of towing point settings, and rarely crash. Why? The lower panels provide dihedral, and given that this is assisted by the forward concentration of sail area that distorts slightly upwards under pressure, one might expect no problems with divergence. The lower panels also act as fins, and since they are placed far apart at the nose and stern, one might expect them to resist yawing and hence resist unstable oscillations.

BOX: box kites share some of the characteristics of Conynes and are well-known for being stable in flight. With lots of vertical surface at the nose and stern, the theory suggests they are not likely to oscillate. However, few have dihedral. Some are flown with two sides of the box vertical, and some are flown with all surfaces inclined diagonally as shown in Figure 1. In the latter case, the upper and lower surfaces could be said to have equal and opposite dihedral and hence might cancel each other out; on the other hand, experiments suggest (Wadsworth, 1997) that box kites have negative weathercocking, which might explain their stability.

ROLLER: One type of roller has fins both at the front and rear. Whatever the reason, it is a text-book example of how to avoid oscillations.

HEXAGON: the simple hexagon kite has no fins, and any dihedral arises from deformation of the frame under wind pressure. One would not expect it to be stable at all, and indeed it isn't. A long tail is essential.

INDIAN FIGHTER: much the same can be said of the Indian fighter kite, which *exploits* instability. An expert flier will vary its direction of movement by letting the line go slack: the kite flattens and it diverges to one side or the other. When it is pointing in the required direction, the line is hauled in, the sails are forced into dihedral, and the kite becomes stable again.

PARAFOIL: military parafoils have been developed using stability theory as the basis for design, with lots of fins in the right places to resist unstable oscillations. They don't generally have dihedral. As one might expect, toy parafoils are vulnerable to divergence.

This kind of argument doesn't really prove anything, but neither does seem to reveal any major contradictions with the theory (if it had, we would have known that a new approach was needed).

So far, we have been looking at how a kite may turn or wobble out of control from side-to-side. Now we need to look at the fore-and-aft direction. As with the previous case, we shall start with the equilibrium conditions and then go on to the problem of dynamic stability.

Longitudinal equilibrium

We have already seen that a kite must have weight in order to fly at all – as little as possible, but nevertheless a finite amount. This is not difficult to manage. But for longitudinal equilibrium, the weight must also be *arranged* correctly. For a kite of any given configuration, it is easier to think of the CG being fixed and look instead at how the other forces on the kite should be related to it. All the forces must be expressed in the same units, so the weight term is expressed as **Mg** where **M** is the mass of the kite and **g** the acceleration due to gravity. If **M** is in kg units and **g** is in ms^{-2}, **Mg** will be in newtons. The other forces are the tension in the flying line **T** and the aerodynamic lift and drag. The lift and drag can be combined into a single resultant force: call it the aerodynamic force **P**.

Fig 9: Triangle of forces

The three forces **Mg**, **T** and **P** must balance, and two conditions are necessary and sufficient to bring this about. The first condition is that the magnitudes and directions of the forces are such that when drawn to scale, they fit together to

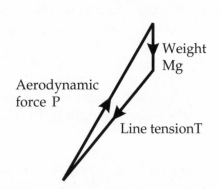

make a triangle (the well-known 'triangle of forces'). It follows that the aerodynamic force must be at a steeper angle than the flying line, otherwise the triangle won't join up (Figure 9).

Fig 10: Intersection of forces

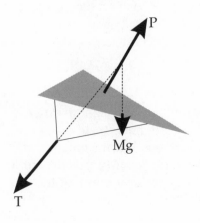

The second condition is that the forces must meet at a point (Figure 10). This would be difficult if the flying line were attached directly to the kite because the aerodynamic force has a will of its own; it tends to move forwards when the angle of attack decreases and backwards when it increases. We solve this by attaching the line via a two-legged bridle or equivalent. If the aerodynamic force moves around, the angle of attack changes until the projection of the flying line passes exactly through the intersection of the weight of the kite and the aerodynamic force.

However, there are limits to how far the aerodynamic force can be allowed to move.

(i) It cannot pass forward of the towing point: if the aerodynamic force were to increase owing to a small increase in wind speed, the kite would rotate clockwise about the towing point and the angle of attack would increase. Usually, this would result in increased **P**, because (over the critical range of values) both lift and drag increase with increasing angle of attack. Hence the kite would continue to rotate: any disturbance would get worse and the kite would flip over.

Fig 11: Relationship between the forces on a kite

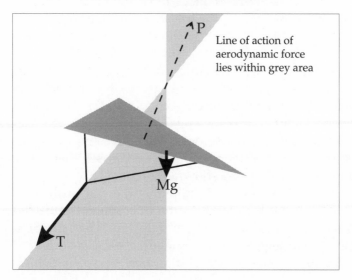

Line of action of aerodynamic force lies within grey area

(ii) Nor can **P** pass rearward of the CG. Actually, we need to be more precise here: Figure 9 shows that the magnitude of **P** must be very much greater than **Mg** in order for the kite to fly at a respectable angle of elevation. Now, consider the towing point as a pivot and, referring to Figure 11, observe that the torque generated by **P** tends to rotate the kite anti-clockwise. It is balanced by the clockwise torque generated by the weight **Mg**. Since the latter is relatively small, its lever arm about the towing point must be correspondingly greater. In this sense, the weight **Mg** must be further aft than the aerodynamic force.

If we refer to the point where the aerodynamic force passes through the kite sail as the Centre of Pressure, then we can summarise the above in terms of a simple relationship:

the towing point, the centre of pressure, and the centre of gravity of the kite must be arranged from nose to stern in that order.

So what are the consequences of all this? Firstly, the mass of the kite must not be concentrated too far forward. Putting it the other way round, the towing point must lie ahead of the CG. This explains why the dimension **a** referred to in the earlier section on lateral stability cannot be negative. Secondly, the aerodynamic force must be sandwiched somewhere in between. We can pin it down more closely if we insist that the kite flies at a certain angle of elevation (70° is respectable) and fix the angle of attack at say 15°. We have now fixed the lines of action of **Mg** and **T**, and since all three forces intersect at a single point we can see that P must lie within the shaded area shown in Figure 11.

Also, as a minor detail, note that the rear bridle leg must be attached to the kite aft of the CG, otherwise the forward leg may go slack. Alternatively, if the line is tied to a fin rather than a two-legged bridle, the fin needs to extend for a reasonable distance along the kite body to achieve an equivalent effect. I am suspicious of kites whose flying line is attached directly to the body – it is difficult to adjust the towing point accurately.

Well, we have gone to a lot of trouble to establish a couple of rather unimpressive facts. Most kitefliers manage without worrying about the relationship between **T**, **P** and **Mg**. If we really wanted to, we could move the CG backwards or forwards by adding ballast at the expense of ruining the kite's efficiency. Much better to adjust the towing point: in practice, John Loy (1994) recommends a towing point located such that the area of sail ahead accounts for 25–33% of the total area, where 'ahead' means in front of the imaginary line perpendicular to the spine that passes through the towing point.

But if the aerodynamic force **P** is in the wrong place *relative to the other two* we are in trouble! In practice it is not easy to determine where **P** is located, and in any case its position changes with the angle of attack. Consequently, we cannot easily plan a new design so as to ensure the right result. However, we can build the kite anyway and if it doesn't work, the analysis does at least tell us what to do next, in particular, if it doesn't fly at a high angle of elevation or if it 'overshoots'.

ANGLE OF ELEVATION

The angle of elevation at which a kite is flying is the angle between the kite, the handler and the ground. Usually, the higher the better, and an important factor is the fore-and-aft adjustment of the towing point (we shall come back to this in more detail in Part 2). Most toy kites fly at an angle of elevation in the range 50°–70°. If our kite can't achieve this even with optimum towing point adjustment, it may be too heavy, or the problem may simply be that the forces are in the wrong places. We have already seen that the line of action of **P** must lie well forward of the CG, and fortunately, the lift force usually locates itself closer to the leading edge than the trailing edge, but some kites such as Eddys and deltas have heavy spars near the front and consequently their CG is well forward too. They would not get very far off the ground unless we could somehow ensure that the aerodynamic force were even closer to the front than the CG.

Figure 12: Billow

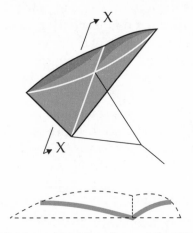

Cross-section through XX

In fact, the leading and trailing edges of a conventional diamond-shaped kite don't stay flat because they are unsupported: there are no spars at the edge to hold them in place. Instead they billow upwards under wind pressure. Coupled with the dihedral angle, this gives the kite a shape more like that of a shallow boat than an aeroplane (Figure 12). As a result the tail is deflected downwards and the nose upwards, or (what amounts to the same thing) the aerodynamic force is shifted forwards – exactly the effect we want to achieve.

With the exception of sleds, almost all kites have unsupported leading edges that keep their noses up in this way. Some Cody kites (box kites with additional wings) have a top sail designed specifically for this purpose. Even delta kites, which have spars along the leading edge for much of the wingspan, have an unsupported section near the nose that tilts upwards relative to the main body of the sail when the structure deforms under wind pressure (see Figure 20: the two diagonal spars do not extend all the way to the nose). Consequently, designing a new type of kite with a continuous leading edge spar represents quite a challenge.

PREVENTING OVERSHOOT

There is another important reason for keeping a kite's nose up. From time to time, the flying line is liable to go slack: for example, during launch, when the handler yanks the line to encourage the kite to climb. It can also happen if the kite reaches a high angle of elevation and an updraft carries it overhead. In either case, there is a danger that the kite will glide forwards like an aeroplane in free flight, leaving the handler with a slack line and a loose grip on events (Figure 13).

Figure 13: Overshoot

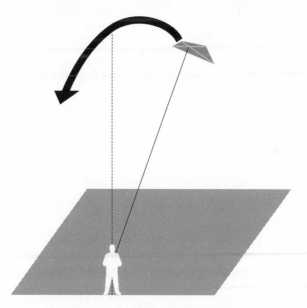

In these circumstances, we really want the kite to sink backwards and away from the handler so as to take up the slack, ie, it *mushes* nose-up. Again, the solution is to keep the aerodynamic force well ahead of the CG. In this sense, kites are quite different from aeroplanes.

Now we turn to the more subtle question of dynamic stability in the longitudinal direction. Longitudinal stability problems don't crop up very often and they are usually easier to cure than lateral ones. I have observed two distinct types with my own kites, the first being a low-frequency oscillation that might be described as repeated overshoot. We shall return to this in a moment.

Figure 14: Pecking

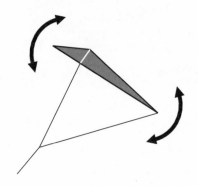

The second is a high-frequency pitching oscillation that seems to correspond to a form of instability identified by Bryant et al (1942) as possibly occurring at high altitudes. The kite 'pecks' backwards and forwards like a farmyard chicken (Figure 14). For a glider type of kite, they recommended damping by increasing the area of tailplane. This suggests that tailless kites with a high aspect ratio (large wingspan compared to their length, like a hang-glider) are more prone to pecking than traditional forms. I have seen a V-shaped kite behave in just this way, but this could also be explained as a resonant mode of vibration in the wings, which were unusually long, narrow, and flexible.

We have already referred to the need for kites to stay nose-up. In some older deltas, the 'billowed' area is relatively small and consequently they are liable to glide forward when they reach a certain altitude. In a light breeze, my old delta sinks gently until the flying line is almost horizontal. Because the flying line is now pulling the towing point forward rather than down, the kite lifts its nose and climbs back up to repeat the cycle again. I doubt whether this repeated overshoot corresponds to any of the theoretical modes of instability identified by Bryant *et al.*

Conclusion

We have now pinpointed the main types of instability that in theory can occur with an idealised kite flying under idealised conditions, and some guidelines have been suggested for avoiding them when working out a new design. In what follows, we shall look at practical methods for modifying or adjusting a kite – whether or not it satisfies the guidelines – so as to get the best out of it.

PART 2: PRACTICAL METHODS FOR ADJUSTMENT AND TRIM

What do you want your kite to do?

If you want to get the best out of your kite, it will help you to work out exactly what you want it to do. Different people want different things. You can choose from:

— steady flight in rough winds

— soaring flight in light breeze (ie, nearly overhead, but you'll need to keep an eye on it)

— not too much pull on the line (you don't want to get carried away)

— ability to carry a payload such as a camera, or tow a buggy (you *do* want to get carried away)

— ease of launch so it goes up without any fuss.

All of these depend on the design, the quality of construction, and the state of adjustment. The design requirements for a stable kite have already been covered in Part 1, so here we shall concentrate on what to do with a kite that you have already bought or made. The quality may be good, bad or indifferent – if it flies, all well and good, but you may be able to make it fly better through minor adjustments. Otherwise you will need to try one or other of the modifications suggested later. The fault chart in figure 23 is intended to provide a quick guide to the problems that can arise and what to do about them.

In particular, a kite that is badly adjusted or distorted may fly in a light breeze but fail to cope with rough winds, so we shall start by explaining something about flying performance and turbulence generally.

Most people want their kites to fly high. One way to do this is to attach it to a long piece of string! But suppose we have two different kites attached to two different lengths of string; how do we tell which is 'best'? What we are really interested is the angle between the kite, the handler, and the ground; we shall call this the *angle of elevation*. We are impressed by a kite that draws the line tight and rises to a position almost overhead, and less impressed by one that doesn't, even if it is actually higher off the ground. In other words, we measure performance in terms of the angle of elevation, and aim to get it as close as possible to 90°.

Two other factors have to be taken into account. First, the angle of elevation depends a great deal on whether the towing point is properly adjusted. We shall come back to this later, but for the moment we shall assume the towing point is set to its optimal position.

Second, the flying line has to be lifted into the air and this constitutes an extra load on any kite. More important, flying lines produce aerodynamic drag – the longer the line, the greater the drag, and this should be taken into account if we are comparing two kites flown on different lengths of line, or lines of a different type.

If we are lucky, our kite will be sufficiently large and powerful that the weight and drag of the line can be ignored. In these circumstances, the angle of elevation tells us something about its aerodynamic efficiency. The lift force, acting vertically upwards, draws the kite overhead. The drag force pulls it downwind. Consequently, a kite flying almost overhead is producing a great deal of lift and very little drag, and it is the ratio of these two forces that aerodynamicists use to measure the efficiency of a wing. If we can estimate the angle of elevation, it so happens that the ratio of lift to drag is approximately the tangent of that angle.

All this assumes that the kite remains firmly glued to its equilibrium position, whereas even the steadiest kite will wander about somewhat. In fact, graceful movement is part of the attraction of kite-flying, and each kite has its own particular signature. So we need to understand a little more about these movements and the air turbulence that causes them.

The flight envelope

Depending on the weather and the shape of the ground over which it is blowing, the wind is turbulent to a greater or lesser degree. Turbulence is caused by the mixing of two layers of air: (a) the *boundary layer* of still air that is trapped close to the ground and (b) the air that is moving at a steady speed higher up. In between, up to a few hundred metres from the ground, the air rolls along in swirling eddies like giant tree trunks rolling down a hillside. The gaps between the larger eddies are filled up by smaller ones rotating in different directions, so that when flying at any particular height, a kite is buffeted by gusts whose strength and direction vary from one moment to the next (Daniels, 1984). We can feel some of them on the ground: the stronger the wind, the larger the eddies and the more violent the gusts.

Turbulence is greatest downstream from hills, trees, and buildings. It may upset the equilibrium of a kite completely, or allow it to sink during a lull. Even if the kite does not crash, turbulence will make it dart about in a way that mathematicians call *chaotic*.

Imagine the path of the kite traced out in the sky over a period of a few minutes. We shall call this the *trajectory*. It would look like a giant scribble, and if we were able to draw a smooth curve – an *envelope* – round the outside, the envelope would have a characteristic size and shape. Figure 15 shows an oval-shaped envelope for an imaginary kite: in practice the shape may be different. Actually, a kite will stray outside almost any envelope if we wait long enough, so it is not really an envelope at all, but a statistical contour that the kite occupies for a given proportion (say 99%) of the time.

Clearly, the size and shape of the envelope tell us a great

Figure 15: Flight envelope

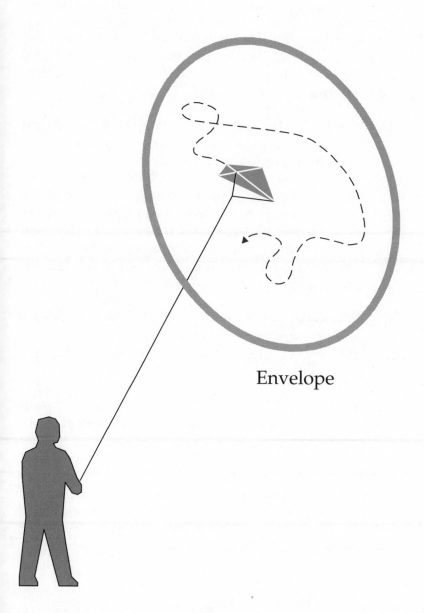

Envelope

deal about the performance of the kite. A well-behaved one will have a small envelope at a high angle of elevation: it stays high in the sky and doesn't wander about very much. We saw in the previous section that a high angle requires lots of lift, minimum weight (including the kite itself and the flying line), and little drag, that is to say, no tail on the kite and a thin flying line. But more is needed if the kite is to stay where we want it, because the size and position of the envelope can change dramatically according to the circumstances.

(i)   It will increase in size in a *strong or turbulent wind* because the wind contains more energy, and its strength and direction are more variable.

(ii)   If the kite is *distorted* perhaps through wear and tear so that its two sides are no longer symmetrical, again the envelope will be larger, and furthermore its position will shift downwards and to one side so that the kite will spend less time at altitude and swoop close to the ground a lot.

(iii)   If the towing point is *not correctly adjusted in the optimum position*, even though the envelope remains compact and correctly aligned downwind, the kite will simply not fly as high as it should.

(iv)   If the kite is *unstable* the envelope will expand downwards to touch the ground (and sooner or later, so will the kite).

So much for the general principles. Now we can get down to the practical business of sorting out a kite that doesn't work. First we'll go through the different types of adjustment and then tie things together at the end with a systematic procedure for diagnosing problems and putting them right.

Lateral adjustment is all about symmetry. We really want the two halves of the kite to be the same so that it flies straight. But most kites suffer from small defects in their construction such as unequal distortion of the spars or stretching of the sails that in turn lead to unequal lift, unequal drag, or unequal weight. This ought not to be a problem with a new kite, but it doesn't take much wear and tear for the thing to go out of kilter. The result is reduced stability, or simply a kite that hugs the ground, leaning annoyingly to one side. Few kites have built-in facilities for lateral adjustment, and the problem is almost never mentioned in the text books. Yet lateral adjustment is just as important as longitudinal adjustment in practice, and there are several ways of achieving it.

In practice, it doesn't seem to matter much whether the problem is caused by unequal lift or unequal drag (cases where the kite is significantly heavier on one side than the other are rare). All we have to do is bias the configuration in some way until the kite flies true. Some suggestions are given in Figures 16 to 20. Figure 16 shows a lateral bridle: it can be adjusted at the towing point via a lark's head hitch in the same way as a fore-and-aft bridle. It seems to work for hexagons and sleds, although the effects with some of my sleds are unpredictable (to make a sled veer to the handler's left, I shorten the left hand leg).

Figure 16: Lateral bridles

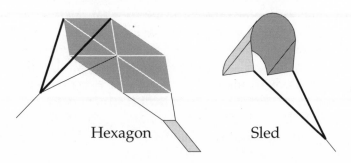

Hexagon   Sled

A different solution is shown in Figure 17. It works for almost any type of kite: we add drag to the wingtip on the side towards which we want the kite to go. A small 'pocket' or spoiler made by sewing or glueing a trapezoidal flap of material to the underside of the sail is the simplest method. It can be adjusted to give varying amounts of bias by stapling or taping it partly closed. The added drag is a disadvantage of course.

Figure 17: Spoiler

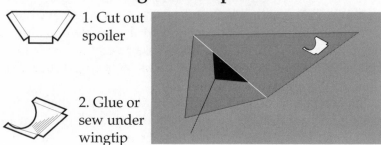

1. Cut out spoiler

2. Glue or sew under wingtip

An Eddy or cutter sail can be adjusted by sewing wide loops to the back of the sail and threading the spar through one or other of the loops so as to bow the spar slightly and change the degree of billow: this biasses the kite towards the side with the greatest billow (Figure 18). Conyne kites are also sensitive to unequal billow and one way of getting round this is shown in Figure 19. The idea is to link the lateral spar at one wingtip with the nearest longitudinal spar. Increasing the tension in the string raises the tension in the leading edge of the sail on the same side, and biasses the kite towards that side. This is perhaps the opposite of what one might expect given what has already been said about the Eddy, but I can't help that.

Finally, a delta kite can be adjusted by sliding the wing spar forwards in its sleeve on the side towards which you want it to go. There is a possible difficulty here – if the sleeve is longer than the spar there is nothing to prevent the spar sliding out of position again after take-off. On the other hand, if it isn't, you won't be able to move it. For a 'long-sleeved'

Figure 18: Adjusting sail tension of Eddy or cutter

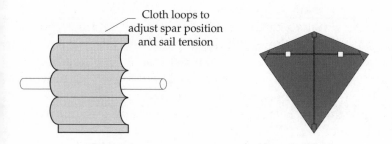

Cloth loops to adjust spar position and sail tension

Figure 19: Tensioning a Conyne sail

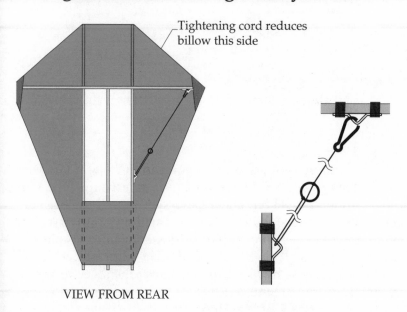

Tightening cord reduces billow this side

VIEW FROM REAR

49

delta you can staple the sail to the spar to keep it in position, but to adjust it further you will have to pull the staples out again. I solved the problem by changing the way the spreader (the lateral spar that keeps the sail spread out) is attached to the rest of the kite (Figure 20). If one adds a piece of string to each end, knotted to the head of a split pin, the pin can be passed through the sail sleeve into any one of several alternative holes drilled into the wing spar. The hole in the sleeve needs to be reinforced with an eyelet to prevent fraying. Also, it is better to glue a reinforcing block to the spar and drill the block rather than risk weakening the spar itself.

Figure 20: Adjusting delta spars

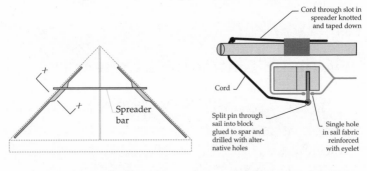

VIEW OF KITE FROM REAR   SECTION THROUGH XX

Longitudinal adjustment: moving the towing point

The most important adjustment you can make to a kite is to move the towing point backwards or forwards. Its fore-and-aft position affects both the angle of elevation (how high the kite will fly), and stability (whether it will fly at all). For kites with a two-legged fore-and-aft bridle, adjustment is simple. Just attach a small ring to the bridle via a lark's head hitch, and move it along by loosening the hitch whenever you want to make an adjustment.

For other types of kite different measures are called for. The flying line of a conventional delta kite is usually attached to the tip of a fin sewn underneath the spine (see the lower diagram in Figure 2). Sometimes an extra loop is provided forward of the tip as an alternative towing point for flying in strong winds, but I have not found loops very useful on my old and battered machines because the fin material stretches with use and the loops are pulled out of position. Reinforcing tape helps, but there is a much better solution.

Figure 21: Adjustable bridles for deltas

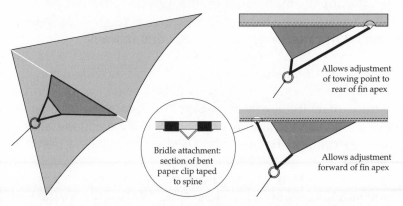

Allows adjustment of towing point to rear of fin apex

Bridle attachment: section of bent paper clip taped to spine

Allows adjustment forward of fin apex

The well-known delta specialist Dan Leigh recommends adding an adjustable bridle with one end attached to the tip of the fin and the other to the spine. Figure 21 shows two possible ways of doing this, together with an alternative method that involves cropping the bottom of the fin and attaching a short bridle to the newly cropped corners. The first two layouts are better, but they require one end of the bridle to be attached to the kite spine, which lies on the other side of the sail. I use an old paper-clip: straighten it out, cut off about 30mm, and bend it into a zig-zag shape as shown in the figure. Cut a small hole in the sail and tape the paperclip to the spine so that it projects downwards through the hole. Four or five turns of tightly wound insulation tape are enough to secure it firmly. Then tie the bridle to it with a bowline knot. The other end of the bridle can be tied to a loop of scrap material sewn to the tip of the fin. I use a rectangle of material about 30mm by10mm, folded lengthways three or four times to give it extra thickness and strength.

Now we are ready to do some adjusting. First let's assume the kite flies steadily and points in the right direction, but it won't climb very far off the ground. It could be that the towing point is too far forward or too far back. Generally speaking the angle of elevation increases as the towing point moves rearwards from the nose of the kite, rising gradually to a peak at a particular setting, and falling quite quickly thereafter. If we want the kite to soar as high as possible we would aim to find the optimum position. Try moving the bridle point just a few millimetres at a time: sometimes a small shift can change performance dramatically.

However if we want to tow a buggy we will need the maximum horizontal towing force. This occurs when the towing point is set well back so that the kite can rise only a limited distance above the ground – it is almost 'face-on' to the wind. The maximum payload capacity for *lifting* objects such as cameras occurs with a setting somewhere between the two.

Now for stability: if the kites flops about or spins uncontrollably without really getting off the ground, it could be laterally unstable. As explained in Part 1, there are two sorts of lateral instability. The first is known as divergence: the kite may rise for some distance, then turn over on its side and dive into the ground. A kite will usually show a preference for one side or the other because of small asymmetries in its construction, although if perfectly made it should show none. Correct the asymmetry as described in the previous section before doing anything else: the problem may simply be distortion of the frame or fabric. Once the kite is 'balanced' and crashing equally often to the left and right, you can be fairly sure that it is unstable rather than just bent. (By now it will probably be broken, unless you remember the golden rule: when a kite is about to crash let the line go slack!) Now you can try moving the towing point forward.

On the other hand, if the towing point is *too* far forward the kite may wobble from side to side, with the wobbles turning into swoops of increasing size until the kite turns right over and spins like a catherine wheel or until it hits the ground. This is the second type of lateral instability – unstable oscillations. Try moving the towing point back.

There is of course no guarantee that you'll find a position for the towing point that (a) eliminates both types of instability, and (b) gives you a reasonable angle of elevation: you may just have a non-flying pig, so on to the next section.

Damping, and other cures for instability

Even an unstable kite can be made to fly if you are prepared to modify it, and you know what type of instability it is suffering from. Sometimes they are difficult to tell apart, but generally speaking divergent instability is a diving crash to one side or the other (think of a skateboard placed on top of a barrel), while unstable oscillations are side-to-side wobbles of increasing intensity. Either can be followed by a spinning movement but a divergent crash usually ends up with the kite hitting the ground hard nose-first.

Divergent instability is partly caused by too much fin area too close to the stern. This was a puzzle to me when I first started kite flying and it resulted in a lot of wasted time and effort until I took the trouble to understand what was really going on. After all, aircraft and weathercocks are designed with fins at the stern in order to keep them in line with the wind – why not a kite also? Well, the answer can be found in Part 1 – all we need to know here is that it can be overcome by increasing the dihedral, moving the fin forward, or a combination of the two. Dihedral is an aeronautical term used to describe the angle at which the wings are tilted upwards on an aircraft. If your kite is flat, you may be able to split the cross-spar in two and join it with an angled junction piece instead, or simply bend the spar upwards on either side using a bowstring (see Figure 4).

Unstable oscillations can also be tackled by increasing the dihedral, and it may help to add fins at the front and rear. Both these 'damp down' the swinging movements typical of unstable oscillations. However, the most elegant solution is to make the kite lighter for the same surface area by replacing the spars with lighter material.

There is a simple cure-all for lateral instability. If all else fails a tail may do the trick. Different types of tail are shown in Figure 3. They all work in the same way, by adding drag that holds the kite in line with the wind, and absorbs energy that might otherwise build up into oscillations. Streamers can be bought from kite shops. Drogues and ribbons you can make yourself out of string, insulation tape and plastic bags. Once, in desperation, I made one by taking off my socks and attaching them to the kite stern via a longish piece of string. Purists prefer not to add a tail if they can help it because of the extra weight, the increased likelihood of tangling, and a general distaste for airborne exhibitionism. But a tail does have advantages. Unlike flapping sails, it can be removed for flying in a light wind. Furthermore, there is no reason why an unstable kite with a tail should not fly better than a stable one without – it may actually be more efficient that way. Keep the tail as light as possible but with sufficient drag to 'damp' down the unstable motion.

Sleds

A sled is prone to collapse in buffeting winds. Sometimes it will turn inside-out, sometimes reopen with a crack like a parachute, and sometimes cross sticks and plummet. It helps to

Figure 22: Stabilising a sled

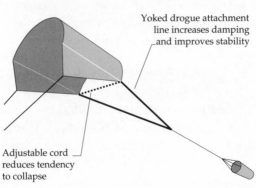

Yoked drogue attachment
line increases damping
and improves stability

Adjustable cord
reduces tendency
to collapse

Figure 23: FAULT CHART

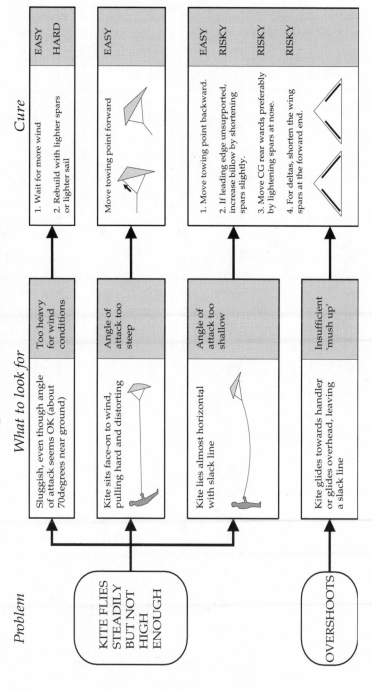

Problem — **What to look for** — **Cure**

KITE FLIES STEADILY BUT NOT HIGH ENOUGH

- Sluggish, even though angle of attack seems OK (about 70 degrees near ground) — Too heavy for wind conditions
  - 1. Wait for more wind — EASY
  - 2. Rebuild with lighter spars or lighter sail — HARD

- Kite sits face-on to wind, pulling hard and distorting — Angle of attack too steep
  - Move towing point forward — EASY

- Kite lies almost horizontal with slack line — Angle of attack too shallow
  - 1. Move towing point backward. — EASY
  - 2. If leading edge unsupported, increase billow by shortening spars slightly. — RISKY
  - 3. Move CG rear wards preferably by lightening spars at nose. — RISKY
  - 4. For deltas, shorten the wing spars at the forward end. — RISKY

OVERSHOOTS

- Kite glides towards handler or glides overhead, leaving a slack line — Insufficient 'mush up'

55

(FAULT CHART continued)

Problem	What to look for		Cure	
Flies steadily but LEANS to left or right	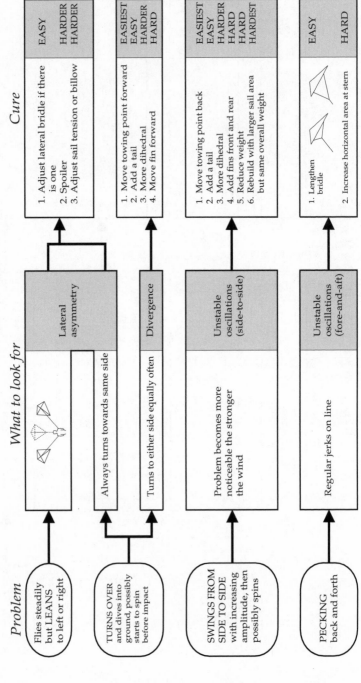	Lateral asymmetry	1. Adjust lateral bridle if there is one 2. Spoiler 3. Adjust sail tension or billow	EASY HARDER HARDER
TURNS OVER and dives into ground, possibly starts to spin before impact	Always turns towards same side	Lateral asymmetry	1. Adjust lateral bridle if there is one 2. Spoiler 3. Adjust sail tension or billow	EASY HARDER HARDER
	Turns to either side equally often	Divergence	1. Move towing point forward 2. Add a tail 3. More dihedral 4. Move fin forward	EASIEST EASY HARDER HARD
SWINGS FROM SIDE TO SIDE with increasing amplitude, then possibly spins	Problem becomes more noticeable the stronger the wind	Unstable oscillations (side-to-side)	1. Move towing point back 2. Add a tail 3. More dihedral 4. Add fins front and rear 5. Reduce weight 6. Rebuild with larger sail area but same overall weight	EASIEST EASY HARDER HARD HARD HARDEST
PECKING back and forth	Regular jerks on line	Unstable oscillations (fore-and-aft)	1. Lengthen bridle 2. Increase horizontal area at stern	EASY HARD

56

tie a piece of string between the spars at the trailing edge as shown in Figure 22, causing a slight funnelling or taper in the cylindrical sail surface, and presumably keeping up the air pressure under the sail so it doesn't deflate so easily. This, of course, increases the drag. A drogue may help, attached via two strings in the form of a V. Incidentally, attaching a drogue to any kite with two strings in this way greatly increases the damping effect, because when the kite veers off-line, the tension passes immediately to one string and the restoring torque is much larger than it would be otherwise.

Summing up: diagnosis and treatment

Let's try and sum up. You take your kite out into a field, launch it, and things go horribly wrong. What to do? Well, there may not be enough wind – it should make the leaves and twigs rustle vigorously on nearby trees without actually bending the trunk – if not, don't bother running up and down the field, just wait for another day. On the other hand, avoid strong, gusty winds, which can make kite-flying a challenge even for experts. If you haven't flown a kite before, now is the time to master the basic skills (there is brief guide to kite-flying at the end). Otherwise, you will know by now that something is wrong with your particular model.

First, a couple of basic checks: make sure the structure is symmetrical and not obviously twisted in some way. Then take the kite into shelter somewhere, grasp the towing point between your fingers, and let the kite hang upside from your hand. It should lie a few degrees from the horizontal, with the nose higher than the stern, and the two sides evenly balanced. This is a rough but useful test to ensure that the centre of mass, the towing point, and probably the centre of pressure are all fairly close together and in the right relationship. It is not foolproof, but if the angle of the kite is a long way out, the chances are that the towing point is a long way from where it should be.

After that, little progress can be made unless you can at

least get the kite off the ground, so move the towing point as far forward as it will go and try again. The kite will probably rise a little way on a slack line, and possibly oscillate. Move the towing point further back until the kite climbs to a satisfactory angle of elevation. If it flies towards you leaving a slack line, or flies over your head ('overshoot'), reduce the weight at the nose by paring down the spars or increase the 'billow' at the leading edge which is necessary to keep any kite nose-up (see Part 1). If it leans to one side or crashes frequently on one side only, you will need to correct for lateral asymmetry. If it crashes equally often on either side, or oscillates, you have a stability problem and you will need to apply one or other of the remedies already referred to. From there on it's a question of fine tuning.

The main steps are summarised in the Fault Chart (Figure 23).

Conclusion

Throughout, we have followed a scientific approach in trying to understand kite behaviour. But kite flying is also an art. A perfectly stable kite may not be much fun: there is more challenge in mastering a skittish kite when it really has no right to stay in the air, like fishing upside down. But the theory helps. It tells us to let the line go slack when things go wrong so as to reduce the wing loading, whereas one's natural reaction is to pull and make things worse. On the other hand, it also tells us to keep the line tight at all times to avoid an overshoot – it's all a matter of timing!

Kite making is an art too. Other things being equal, kites will fly better if well made. Some are exquisite: enthusiasts match their spars carefully for weight and flexibility and take enormous trouble over the cutting and sewing of their sails. After all, kites are beautiful objects in their own right and pride in craftsmanship adds to the pleasure. But not all of us have the time or the facilities needed for this standard of construction, nor can we afford the more expensive products offered in kite stores today. A little understanding of how imperfect kites misbehave is therefore worthwhile.

Unfortunately, or fortunately perhaps, this is not the end of the story. No-one *really* understands kite behaviour: there is plenty of room for new designs, and if yours break the rules, so much the better!

References

BRYANT L W (1937) *Nomenclature for stability coefficients.* Aeronautical Research Council, Reports and Memoranda 1801.

BRYANT L W, W S BROWN and N E SWEETING (1942) *Collected researches on the stability of kites and towed gliders.* Aeronautical Research Council, Reports and Memoranda 2303.

FRAZER R A and W J DUNCAN (1929) *On the criteria for the stability of small motions.* Proc Royal Soc Series A, vol 124A, 642-654.

DANIELS A (1984) *Turbulence analysis of kite wind measurements.* Proceedings of European Wind Energy Conference, Commission of the European Community, Hamburg, 22-26 October 1984, 91-95.

LOY J (1994) *On the bridle path (letter to the editor).* American Kite Association Newsletter, 16 (1), 6.

NATHE G A (1967) *Analysis of the para-foil.* AIAA Student Journal, 5 (1), 4-9.

NICOLAIDES J D, R J SPEELMAN and G L C MENARD (1970) *A review of para-foil applications.* J Aircraft, 7 (5), 423-431.

WADSWORTH N (1995) *Personal communication.*

WADSWORTH N (1997) *Personal communication*

Further reading

EDEN M (1989) *Kiteworks: explorations in kite building and flying.* New York: Sterling.
ITO T AND MAKURA H (1983) *Kites, The Science and Wonder.* Tokyo: Japan Publications Inc.

MOULTON R and LLOYD P (1997) *Kites: a practical handbook.* 1st ed Hemel Hempstead: Argus. 2nd ed 1997 Nexus Special Interests ISBN 1-85486 143 3.

PELHAM D (1976) *The Penguin book of kites.* Harmondsworth: Penguin.

VAN VEEN H (1996) *The Tao of kite flying (the dynamics of tethered flight).* Randallstown: Aeolus Press.

WRIGHT C C (1995) *Kites and transport: coming down to earth?* Universities Transport Study Group Annual Conference, University of Cranfield, January 1995 (unpublished).

THE BASICS OF KITE-FLYING

Safety do's and don'ts

- don't fly in a strong wind

- the wind is turbulent near houses and trees – so keep well clear!

- don't fly if it is raining, and particularly if there is any possibility of thunder (wet kites attract lightning)

- don't fly near electricity pylons, or overhead wires of any kind

- don't fly anywhere near an airfield: it is illegal

- don't fly over roads, buildings, water, or anywhere that you can't safely retrieve the kite if it crashes

- don't let the line run through your fingers: it may cut them.

Launching

It is best to unwind about 30 metres of line first, and get a friend to carry the kite downwind. First make sure the kite is pointing upwards, with the front facing you, and that the tail is not tangled with the line. When you are ready, signal to launch. This is easier and more elegant than running along with the kite. As soon as the kite is clear of the ground, draw in some line hand-over-hand to make it rise. The wind is usually stronger higher up, and you can pay the line out when the kite starts to pull.

Control

If the line goes slack, a kite will lose its sense of direction. You have to keep the line tight at all times. If the breeze drops and the kite flops about, wait until it is pointing the right way (ie, up) and then haul in the line. The kite should then move in the desired direction.

On the other hand, kites need surprisingly little wind to stay up, and can be difficult to manage in stronger ones. If things get difficult you can either (a) reduce height, or (b) abandon operations until the weather improves. If you persist and the kite heads for somewhere it shouldn't, let the line go slack. You can do this by stepping towards the kite or paying out some line. Haul in the line again or step back only when the kite is pointing where you want it to go. In a strong wind it may be difficult to haul in the line again once you have let it out, because the kite will now be higher up where the wind is even stronger. Better to peg the line to the ground and 'walk it down' with the line passing under your armpit. Above all, if a kite power-dives towards the ground, DON'T PULL! Let the line go slack, by taking a few steps forward. This will avert a crash. Probably.

As it happens, these are the basic principles used when flying Indian fighter kites. Skilled pilots can manoeuvre them in any direction, even though they have only a single line.

Finally, if two kite lines cross, both fliers should walk slowly towards one another and (if necessary) circle round in a friendly way until the lines uncross.

GLOSSARY

There follows a list of some technical terms used here or elsewhere, with non-technical explanations.

aerodynamic force: the overall force on an object caused by the motion of a fluid (air is a 'fluid') around it.

aspect ratio: see *ratio*.

boundary layer: when a fluid moves along a solid surface, the layer immediately next to the surface 'sticks' to it. The thickness of the sticky layer depends on the roughness of the surface, among other things.

centre of gravity: the earth's gravitational pull acts separately on the atoms and molecules of which an object is made. But it is possible to represent all the material as being concentrated at a particular point, the *centre of gravity*. Engineers are grateful for this otherwise they would have to know about every molecule in your body in order to design a stool.

chaos: some variables fluctuate in a way that looks 'random' but in fact they are undergoing changes that might in principle be calculated if we knew every detail of what was happening. Imagine running a film of a kite flying starting from a known position with all the movements in the surrounding airstream specified. Using aerodynamic theory it ought to be possible to predict what will happen in each subsequent frame of the film. In practice however, if the influences are non-linear and we imagine the process starting again with just a tiny change in the conditions at the start, the process will eventually produce a completely different picture at some time in the future. The weather is chaotic and so are the movements and eddies of the atmosphere at any particular point above the earth's surface. It follows that when a butterfly flaps its wings in Malaysia, a kite could well crash in a violent wind gust over Basingstoke three weeks later. This is not much help to kitefliers.

coefficients, equations, functions and formulae: a mathematical expression in which a variable appears is said to be *function* of that variable: for example, if we drop a water bomb from a kite that falls vertically with constant acceleration **g**, the distance that it travels in time **t** is given roughly by **$gt^2/2$**.

Here the expression **$gt^2/2$** is a function of **t**. It could also be described as a *formula* for distance travelled: a mathematical rule for calculating the unknown distance given the known rate of acceleration and time elapsed since release.

If we know that two things are always equal we can write them in the form of an *equation*: in the above example, it can be shown that the distance travelled, which we can call **s**, is always equal to **$gt^2/2$** and hence we can write the equation **$s = gt^2/2$**. Equations are handy because they can be turned inside-out: here, a bit of juggling reveals that **$t = (2s/g)^{0.5}$** so that we can now treat **t** as the unknown and investigate how it changes when we specify different distances through which the bomb might fall. In particular, if we know the kite is flying say 50m up, we can solve the equation for **t**, in other words, calculate how long we have to get out of the way. There is no other way of doing this other than getting wet.

Here we are worried about a particular bomb moving with a particular rate of acceleration so that **g** is a constant even though we haven't said what its value might be; in an expression such as **$gt^2/2$** where the varying part **$t^2/2$** is multiplied by a constant **g**, the constant is described as a *coefficient* (as it happens, the number **1/2** is also a coefficient).

constant: a quantity or measurement that for the purposes of the analysis we are going to assume fixed even if we have to nail it to the floor.

damping stops things vibrating or oscillating by absorbing their energy of motion, for example an automobile shock absorber modifies the action of the springs so the passengers don't shake like jelly.

degrees of freedom is a term that can take on different meanings depending on the problem to which it is applied. In mechanics, it represents the number of different ways in which a thing can move. A pendulum has one degree of freedom (rotation in one plane), a hovercraft has three (forwards/backwards, side-to-side, and spinning round when the captain wants to show off). A telegraph pole should preferably not have any.

differential equations: a differential equation involves *rates of change* of the unknown variable(s): this is not a definition but it will have to do. A linear differential equation is linear in the rates of change.

A differential equation that involves only rates of change is *first-order*. But rates of change can themselves be changing, and if the equation involves rates of change of rates of change, it is *second-order*. And rates of change of rates of change can themselves be changing . . .

dimensional analysis: most physical quantities have units attached to them: distances can be measured in meters and weights in kilograms. However some quantities are made up of products and ratios such that the units cancel each other out. Dimensional analysis is a clever way of finding fundamental quantities in physics, by looking for combinations of variables that have no dimensions. Only a limited number of combinations are possible and the resulting quantities often turn out to have practical significance: Reynolds' Number for fluid flow in a tube is a good example, being the product of the tube diameter, the velocity of flow, and the fluid density, divided by its viscosity – the nature of the flow changes from turbulent to laminar at a critical value of this number.

discriminant: the discriminant of an equation or a set of simultaneous equations is a mathematical expression whose value says something important about the solutions. For example, the discriminant of the quadratic equation $ax^2 + bx + c = 0$ is $(b^2 - 4ac)$. If its value is negative the two solutions are not 'real', whereas if it is zero the two solutions are identical.

drag or air resistance: the component of aerodynamic force acting against the motion of the body and hence resisting its progress.

eddy: revolving motion in a fluid. You can see eddies when rowing a boat – the water swirls around a vertical axis at the oar tips.

force measures the amount of 'push' or 'pull' given to an object: if there were no restraining force on the object such as friction it would start to move, and continue accelerating while the force were applied. Under the action of a given force, a massive object will accelerate sluggishly, while a less massive object will accelerate more sharply, so it is natural to measure force in terms of mass times acceleration. Newtons are commonly used.

lever arm: see *torque, moment and lever arm.*

lift is the component of aerodynamic force acting at rightangles to the general direction of motion of the fluid in which an object is immersed: for an aircraft flying horizontally it acts against the pull of gravity and keeps it in the air.

linear equations: an equation is said to be *linear* in any particular variable if that variable appears only in unadulterated form: it can appear in one or more terms that are added together, multiplied by constants (or other variables), but not raised to a power other than 1. For example, the equation referred to earlier under the heading *coefficients...* is linear in **g** but not in **t**.

mass represents the amount of 'stuff' in an object, and except in nuclear reactions it never changes while the object remains intact wherever the object might be. For engineering purposes, the kilogram is a commonly used unit of mass.

mathematics strikes terror into the heart of many right-thinking people. Others see it as a pleasant pastime. But think about this. Distant parts of the universe may be made of different stuff, obey different laws of physics, and support weird forms of life that are not addicted to lottery programmes on TV. But *everywhere* it is the case that $e^{i\pi} = -1$. Suppose we could communicate with living creatures in the Andromeda galaxy. Initially, the only thing would have in common would be mathematical ideas, and we'd probably start by chatting about sums.

percentiles in statistics are like fuzzy fences: they indicate the limits between which a random variable lies with a given probability. A goat will stray outside its field from time to time but if one measures its position at different times during the day, most of the values will lie within a convenient radius of its food trough.

plane: an imaginary flat surface that goes on interminably in all directions.

projection of a straight line: where the line would go if one carried on drawing it.

proportionality: two *variables* are proportional if a percentage change in one of them is always accompanied by a percentage change in the other of the same amount: for example, the weight of a kite sail made out of a given material is proportional to its area because if you double the area you also double the weight. Incidentally the *ratio* of the two remains constant whatever the values of the variables themselves.

ratio: what you get when you divide one quantity by another (for example, the *aspect ratio* of a wing is its length measured at rightangles to the direction of travel divided by its width from the leading edge to the trailing edge).

resolution of forces: if several different forces act on an object (for example, a kite is subjected to aerodynamic forces together with its weight and the tension in the flying line) we can represent their joint effect as a single force by a process known as *resolution*. If the resultant force is not zero, the kite will accelerate in the direction of the force.

second moment of area: the stiffness of a beam in bending depends to some extent on the shape of its cross-section, and its second moment of area in particular. To calculate it for a beam with symmetrical cross-section, split up the area into very small pieces and multiply the area of each piece by the square of its distance from the axis of symmetry.

simultaneous equations: simultaneous equations are sets of equations governing the values of *two* or more unknowns; usually, none of the equations tells us how to calculate either directly, but their values can still be deduced using one or other mathematical technique.

stress is a way of expressing *force* in a common unit of currency, namely force per unit area. The stress you generate in a brick when you stand on it is similar to that occurring in each of the bricks in a masonry arch when a railway locomotive passes over it. Using stress allows one to make a fair comparison between two different situations. You can safely stand on a disused railway viaduct but don't try to support the locomotive on a single brick.

symmetry: a thing is symmetrical if you can divide it by a *plane* into two halves that are mirror images of one another: things can have more than one plane of symmetry but kites (and kitefliers) generally have just one, passing through the central spine or longitudinal axis. But some kites are not symmetrical at all.

tension: a force that tends to pull something apart (rather than squashing it together) is said to act in *tension*. The tension in your kite line should always be less than your body weight, otherwise you will become a hang-glider pilot.

torque, moment and lever arm: torque and moment are alternative expressions for twisting forces, of the sort that a nut feels when you tighten it with a spanner. The twisting action can be achieved by means of an ordinary 'pushing' force acting on the end of a lever, as happens when you wield your spanner. The distance of your hand from the nut is the *lever arm*: given a constant push, the longer the lever arm, the greater the torque and the tighter the nut.

triangle of forces: all forces have size and direction, and can be represented on paper by arrows drawn pointing in the desired directions with their lengths proportional to the various sizes. If only two forces act on something that is in equilibrium, they are equal and opposite, so the two arrows (pointing in opposite directions) meet at a point. If there are three forces, they can be drawn in the form of a triangle with the arrows pointing in the same direction around the circumference. Consequently, if you know two of them, you can estimate the third by drawing the first two and joining up the triangle (the point of the first arrow must be drawn so as to meet the tail of the second, or vice versa – it doesn't matter which).

variable: another quantity or measurement (such as the tension in a kite line) that has an irritating tendency to change whether we want it to or not.

washout: a wing may be deliberately twisted so that the angle of attack decreases towards the tip in order to reduce the propensity to stall: this happens naturally with the sails of kites and hang-gliders.

weight: the weight of something is the force that it imposes vertically on the ground owing to gravitational pull. For everyday purposes we express it in terms of mass (eg kilograms), but whereas mass is constant, the force actually varies according to location (slightly lower at the earth's equator than at the poles, much smaller on the moon, and virtually zero in deep space). If we are analysing the behaviour of structures such as kites that are affected both by their weight and by other external forces, it is essential to convert the weights to force units (eg newtons) so that all the influences are expressed on the same scale of measurement.